We Live

Primer 1

to accompany
Learning to Read

Writers:

LuAnne D. Yeager, Ruth Hobbs, Dorothy Nisly

CHRISTIAN LIGHT EDUCATION
A division of Christian Light Publications, Inc.
Harrisonburg, Virginia 22802   (540) 434-0750

 **Sunrise Second Edition**

We Live, Primer Series—Book 1

Christian Light Education, a division of
Christian Light Publications, Inc., Harrisonburg, VA 22802
© 2009 by Christian Light Publications, Inc.
All Rights Reserved.
Printed in the United States of America

2nd Printing, 2010

Artist: Charity Hoover
Cover Design: David Miller

ISBN: 978-0-87813-861-6

Contents

Note to the Reader:

The bold and underlined words relate to
Christian Light Education's *Learning to Read* program.

We Live

Primer 1

At the Dam

Dad

Sam

<u>Many</u> <u>for</u> Dad

Do some for Sam.

Do some for Dad.

For Dad

For Sam

Sad Sam

For Dad

For Sam

<u>For</u> Dad

Fat Tam

Sam

Dad

Tam

Mom

Challenge word: **Mom**

Fat Tam sat.

Mom sat at <u>the</u> .

Dad sat at <u>the</u> .

Sam sat at <u>the</u> .

Good . Good .

Good .

Tam!

Dad!

Sad Tam.

Sad Sam.

<u>Good</u> **Mom**.

Nan

Tag

Nan

Nan got <u>the</u> mat.

Nan got <u>the</u> mop.

Nan got Sam.

Sam sat.

Tag got Nan.

Nan got Tag.

<u>Now</u> Dad got Nan.

<u>Good</u> Nan.

<u>Good</u> Sam, <u>Good</u> Pam

Pam sat at <u>the</u> mat.

Sam sat at <u>the</u> mat.

<u>D</u>o not nap <u>now</u>, Pam.

<u>D</u>o not nap <u>now</u>, Sam.

Do good <u>to</u> Tam.

Do good <u>to</u> Tag.

31

Mom put the pan for Tam at
the mat. Mom put the pan
for Tag at the mat.

Pam got <u>the</u> pan <u>for</u> fat Tam.

Sam got <u>the</u> pan <u>for</u> tan Tag.

Good Pam. Good Sam.

Mom got <u>some</u> pop <u>for</u> Sam.

Mom got <u>some</u> pop <u>for</u> Pam.

<u>Good</u> Tom

Tom ran <u>for</u> <u>the</u> rat.

<u>The</u> rat ran <u>for</u> <u>the</u> pot.

Tom ran <u>to</u> <u>the</u> pot.

<u>The</u> rat ran <u>for</u> <u>the</u> rag.

Tom ran <u>to</u> <u>the</u> rag.

The rat ran <u>for</u> <u>the</u> mop.

Tom ran <u>to</u> <u>the</u> mop.

<u>The</u> rat ran <u>to</u> <u>the</u> top.

<u>Now</u> Tom sat.   Tom got sad.

Tom! <u>Here</u>, Tom!

Ron had hot ham <u>for</u> Tom.

Tom ran <u>for</u> <u>the</u> mat.

<u>Good</u> Tom.